Early Maths

Here's a short note for parents:
We recommend that you work through our books with your child, offering guidance and encouragement along the way. Try to find a quiet place to sit, preferably at a table, and encourage your child to hold his or her pencil correctly. Try to work at your child's pace and avoid spending too long on any one page or activity. Most of all, emphasise the fun element of what you are doing and enjoy this special and exciting time!

Illustrated by Jeannette O'Toole
Cover design by Dan Green
Educational consultant Nina Filipek

www.autumnchildrensbooks.co.uk

Get ready to count...

When we have lots of things, we like to count them!
But sometimes it's not so easy...

Octopus tried to count his legs, but he found it was a knotty problem.

Leopard tried to count his spots, but it made him see spots in front of his eyes!

Can you help Octopus count his legs and help Leopard count his spots? Point to the numbers and say them.

2
3
4
5
6
7
8
9
10

Place your reward sticker here

Buckle my shoe

Find a door sticker.

There are rhymes to help Octopus and Leopard learn to count. Here's one of them.

1,2, buckle my shoe.

3,4, knock at the door.

5,6, pick up sticks.

7,8, lay them straight.

9,10, a speckled hen.

How many eggs has the speckled hen laid?

What can you see?

Count up to **3**, what can you see?

Find a bee sticker and a star sticker.

Count up to **3** – birds in the tree.

Count up to **5** – bees in the hive.

Place your sticker here

Count up to **7** – stars in heaven.

Place your sticker here

Count up to **9** – clothes on the line.

Count **10** or more – shells on the shore.

Place your reward sticker here

How many shells on the shore?
Were there more than **10**?

Crazy creatures

How many crazy creatures are there?
Count each line of animals and circle the number.

1 2 3 4 5 6 7 8 9 10

1 2 3 4 5 6 7 8 9 10

1 2 3 4 5 6 7 8 9 10

1 2 3 4 5 6 7 8 9 10

Place your reward sticker here

How many legs?

How many legs do you have? Only two!

Find a spider sticker.

Which of these animals has the most legs?
Count the legs. Write the number.

bird

spider

Place your sticker here

fly

beetle

Draw more

Draw more legs to make the same number on each insect.

Place your reward sticker here

Counting down

Write the missing numbers for the countdown from **10** to **1**.

10

9

◯

7

6

◯

4

3

◯

1

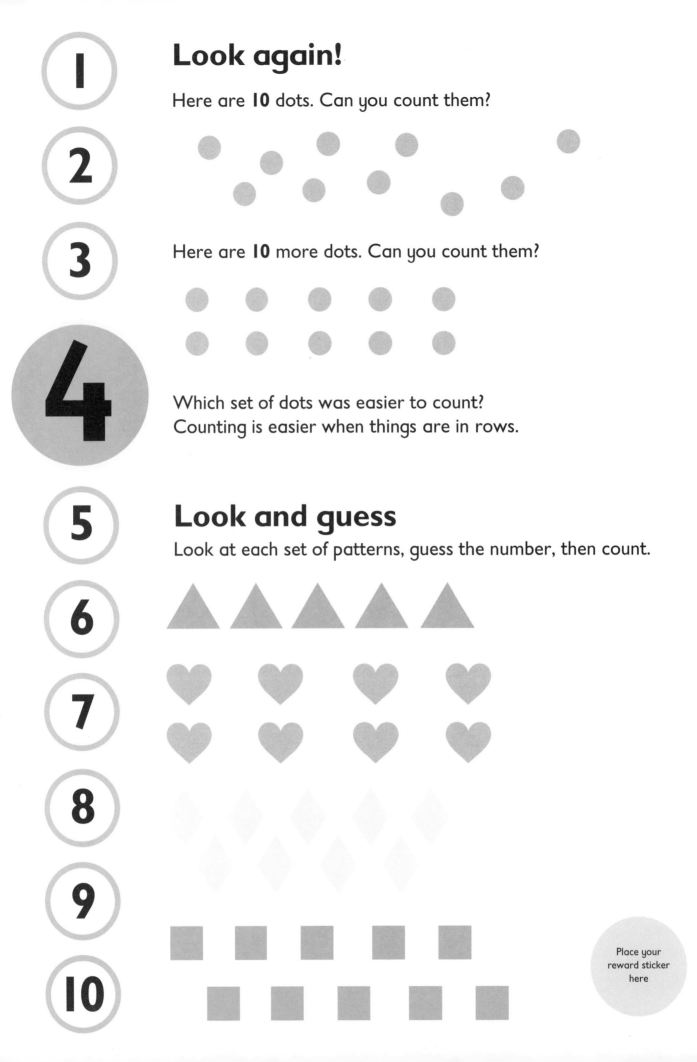

Look again!

Here are **10** dots. Can you count them?

Here are **10** more dots. Can you count them?

Which set of dots was easier to count?
Counting is easier when things are in rows.

Look and guess

Look at each set of patterns, guess the number, then count.

Number patterns

Find a diamond sticker.

Copy each pattern, then guess the number of shapes you have drawn.
Write the number in the box.

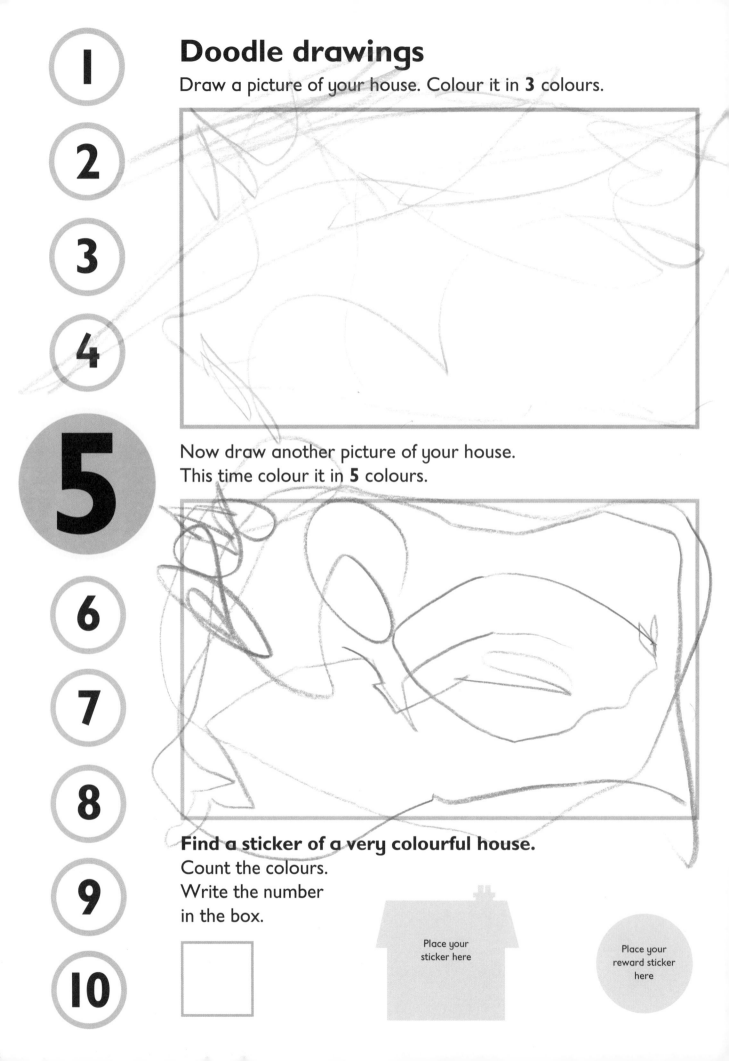

Doodle drawings

Draw a picture of your house. Colour it in **3** colours.

Now draw another picture of your house.
This time colour it in **5** colours.

Find a sticker of a very colourful house.
Count the colours.
Write the number
in the box.

1
2
3
4
5
6
7
8
9
10

Place your
sticker here

Place your
reward sticker
here

Birds of a feather flock together

Birds that look the same want to be together.

Find a bird sticker.
Looks at these birds.
Answer the counting questions.

Place your
sticker here

How many birds...

... have long tails?

... have curly tails?

... have short tails?

... have bushy tails?

Place your
reward sticker
here

Looking at shapes

Can you make a circle shape with your hands and fingers? Can you make a triangle shape?

Here are some names for different shapes.

square	circle	triangle	rectangle

Shapes all around

Find a sticker of a plate. What shape is it?
Draw a line to connect the plate to the matching shape.

Place your sticker here

Find a sticker of a window. What shape is it?
Draw a line to connect the window to the matching shape.

Place your sticker here

Place your reward sticker here

Robot shapes

Find a sticker of a robot's head.

Can you see the shapes that make up the robot?

Place your sticker here

Count the shapes in the robot picture.
Write the numbers in the boxes.

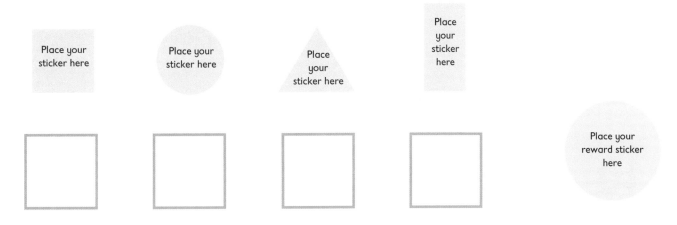

Sorting shapes

Round shapes here, square shapes there.
There are shapes everywhere!

Colour the shapes with **4** sides yellow.
Colour the shapes with **3** sides blue.
Colour the other shapes red.

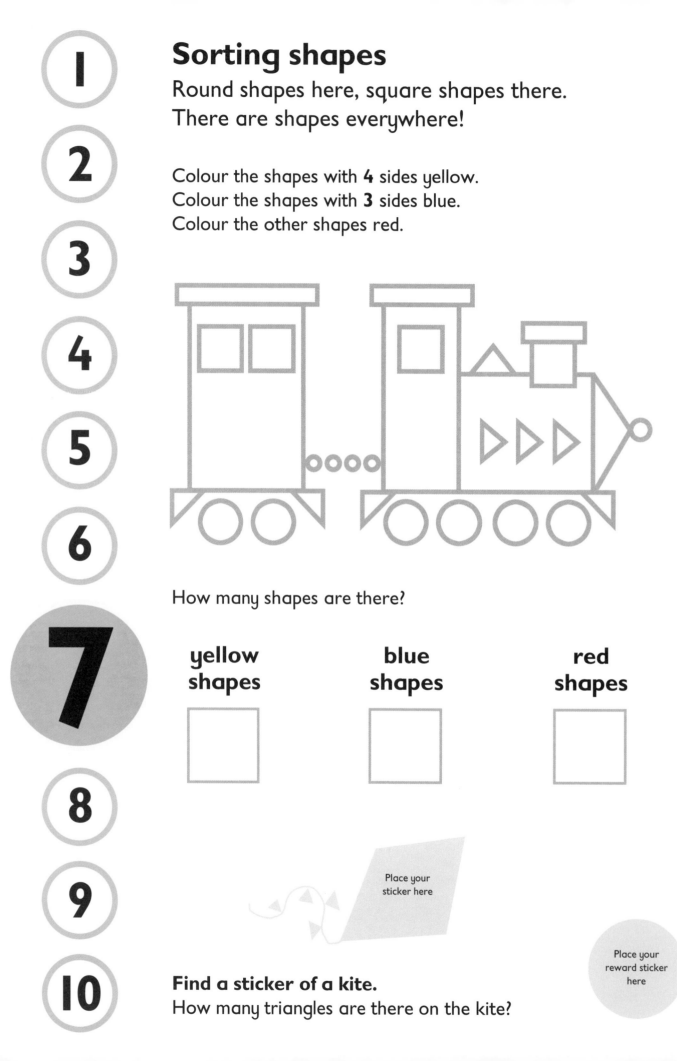

How many shapes are there?

**yellow
shapes**

**blue
shapes**

**red
shapes**

Place your
sticker here

Place your
reward sticker
here

Find a sticker of a kite.
How many triangles are there on the kite?

Terrible twins

Draw the missing shapes to make the robots the same.

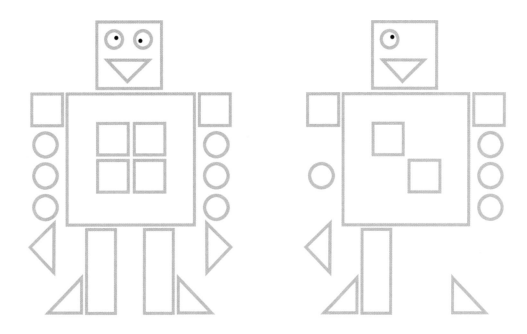

Matching shapes

Colour the two shapes in each line that are exactly the same.

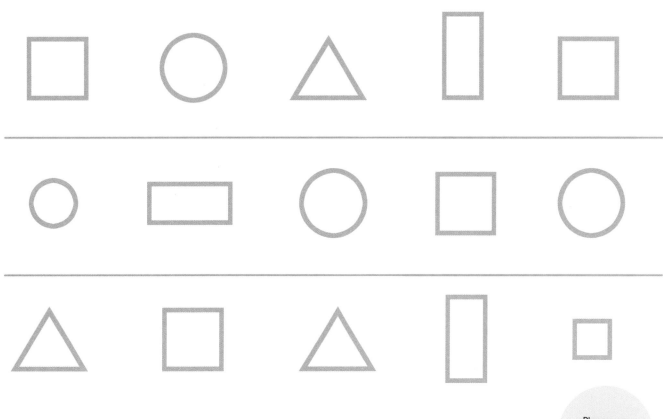

Place your
reward sticker
here

Patterns

We can put shapes and numbers in a row to make patterns.

Draw the missing shape in this pattern.

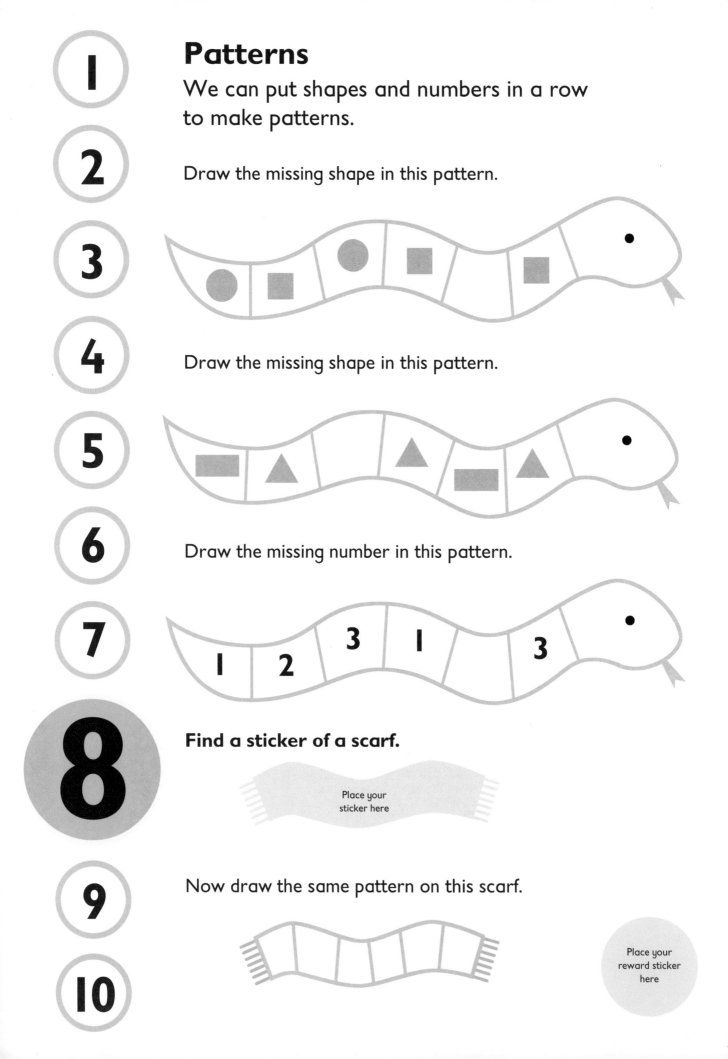

Draw the missing shape in this pattern.

Draw the missing number in this pattern.

Find a sticker of a scarf.

Place your sticker here

Now draw the same pattern on this scarf.

Place your reward sticker here

 Clever me!
 That's right!
 Well done!
 OK!
 Well done!

 I did it!
 Well done!
 That's right!
 Clever me!
 I did it!

 OK!
 Clever me!
 I did it!
 OK!
 Well done!

 I did it!
 That's right!
 OK!
 Well done!
 Clever me!

 Well done!
 OK!
 Clever me!
 I did it!
 That's right!

 OK!
 I did it!
 Well done!
 OK!
 Clever me!

 That's right!
 Clever me!
 OK!
 I did it!
 That's right!

Same on both sides

Colour the butterfly's
wings so that they are
the same on both sides.

Finish the pictures

Trace the dotted lines to finish these shapes.

What size?

When we want to know the size of something, we measure it.

Find a sticker of a tree.

Which is the tallest tree? Colour it in.

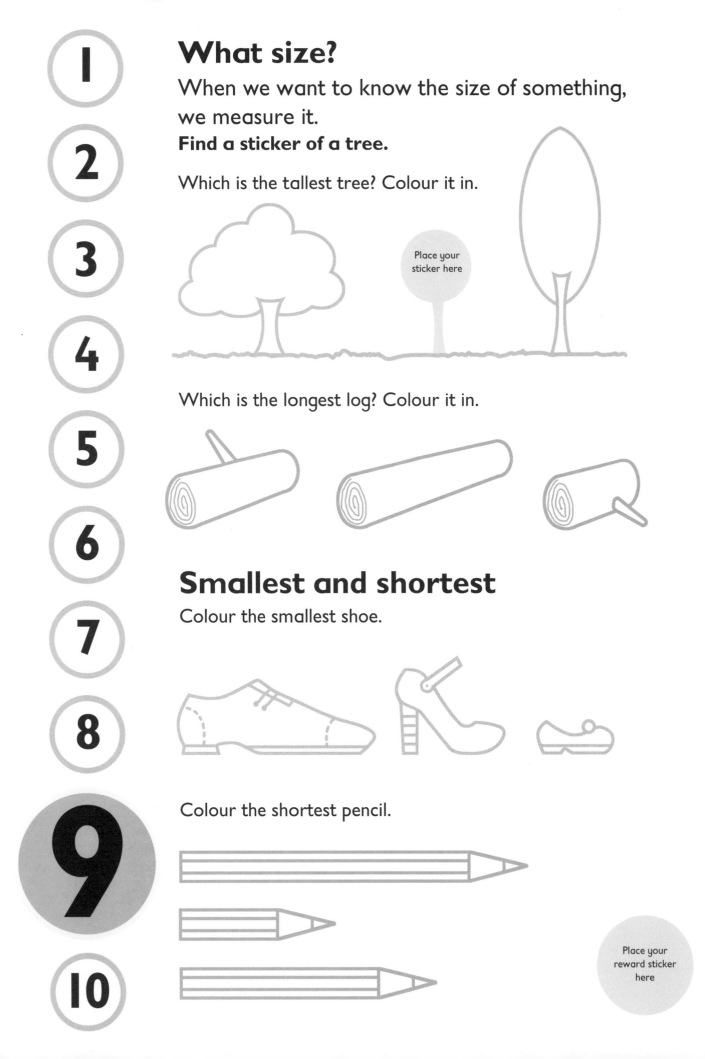

Which is the longest log? Colour it in.

Smallest and shortest

Colour the smallest shoe.

Colour the shortest pencil.

Place your sticker here

Place your reward sticker here

1 2 3 4 5 6 7 8 9 10

Fitting in

Find a sticker of a cereal box.
How many cereal boxes can fit in the cupboard? Draw them.

Find a sticker of a van.
How many vans fit in the tower? Draw them.

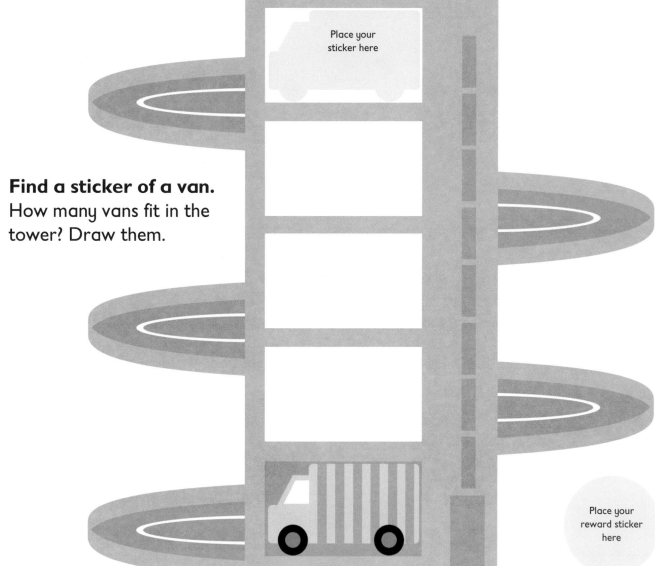

Place your sticker here

Place your reward sticker here

First and last

Find a sticker to finish the picture.

Look for clues to tell you what the sticker might be. In this picture story what comes first, what comes next, what comes last? Write **1, 2** and **3** in the boxes.

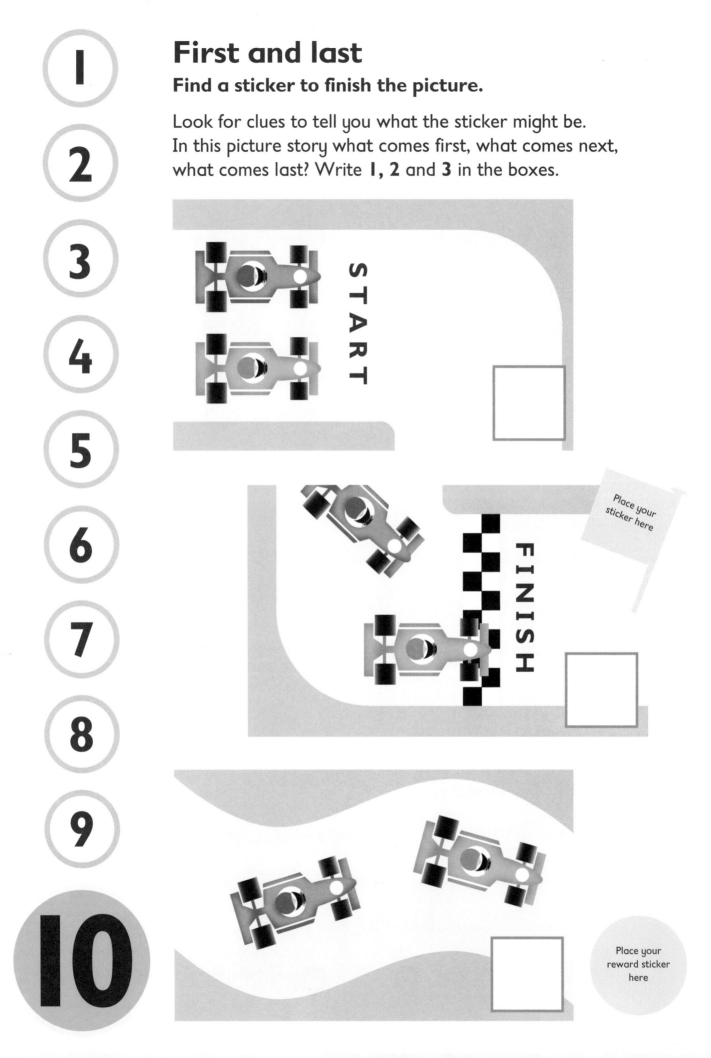

Long time or short time?

Find an ice cream sticker.

How long does it take to do these things?
Which of these things take a short time? Which take a long time?
Draw a line from each picture to the **'short time'** or **'long time'** box.

Watch your favourite
TV programme.

Build a house.

Sing a song.

short time

Learn how
to be a doctor.

long time

Grow a tree
from a seed.

Fly around
the world.

Place
your
sticker
here

Eat an
ice cream.

Place your
reward sticker
here

Draw 1 more. What's the score?

Draw 1 more thing in each line, then count them.
Write the number.

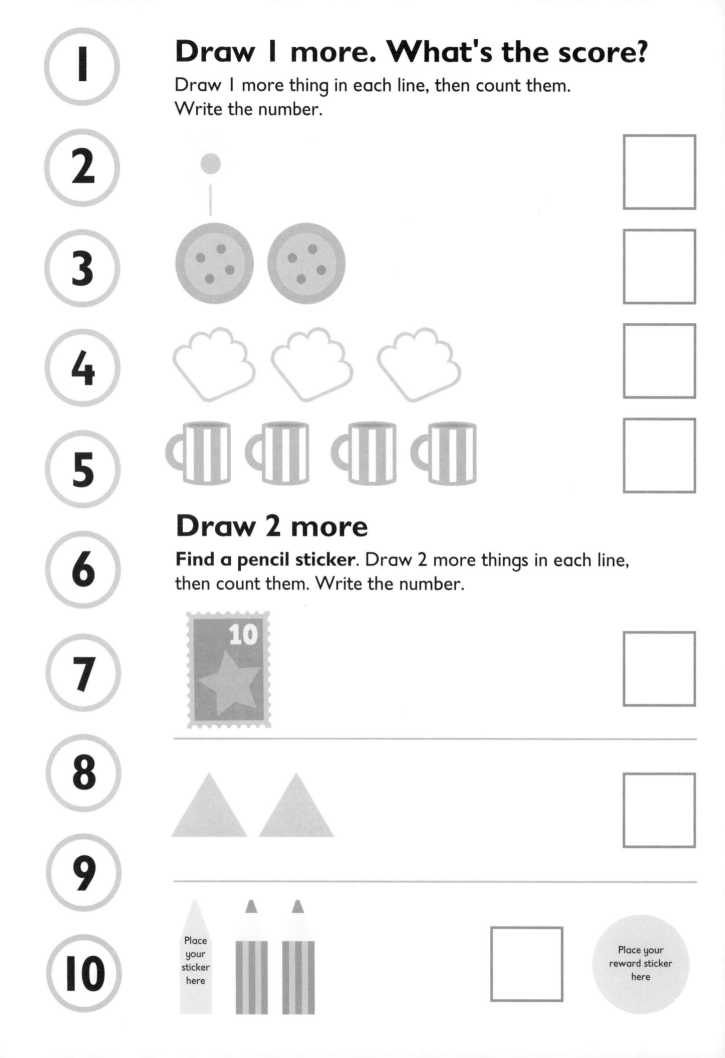

Draw 2 more

Find a pencil sticker. Draw 2 more things in each line, then count them. Write the number.

Adding sums

Here are some adding sums for you to try.
Count the pictures in each line and write the answer.

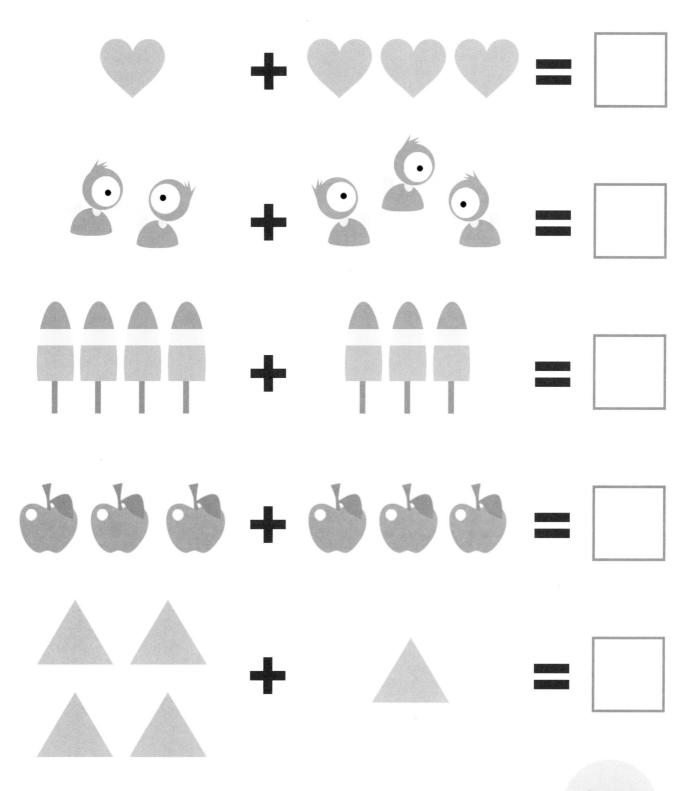

Draw 4 more

Find a snail sticker.

Draw 4 more to finish the adding sums. Write the answers.

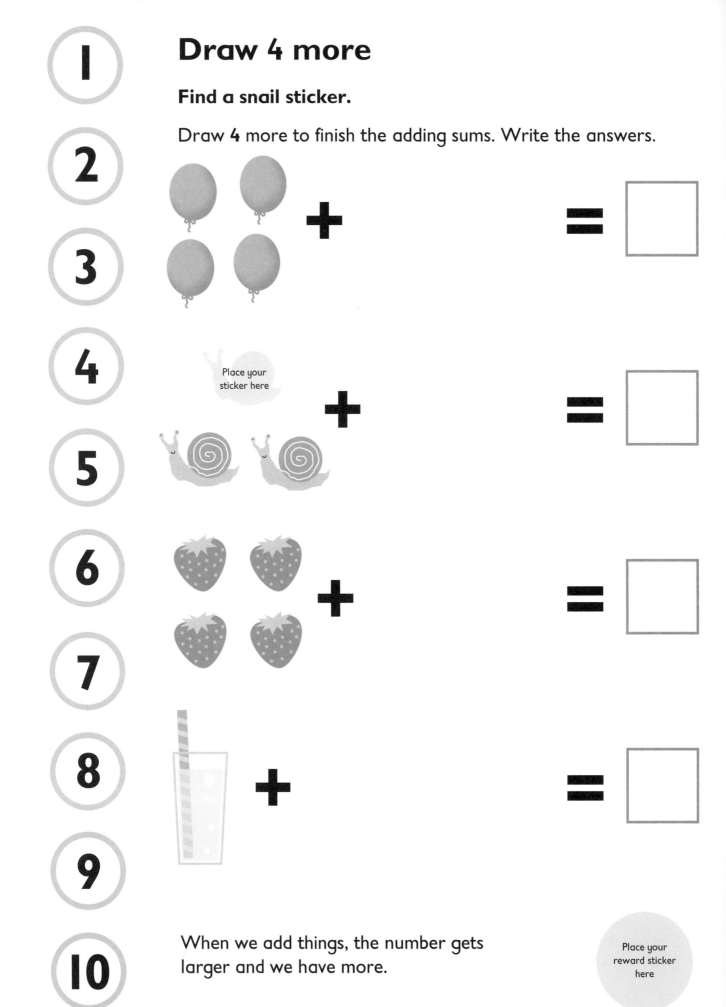

When we add things, the number gets larger and we have more.

Place your reward sticker here

Making 5

How many are there altogether? Write the answers in the boxes.

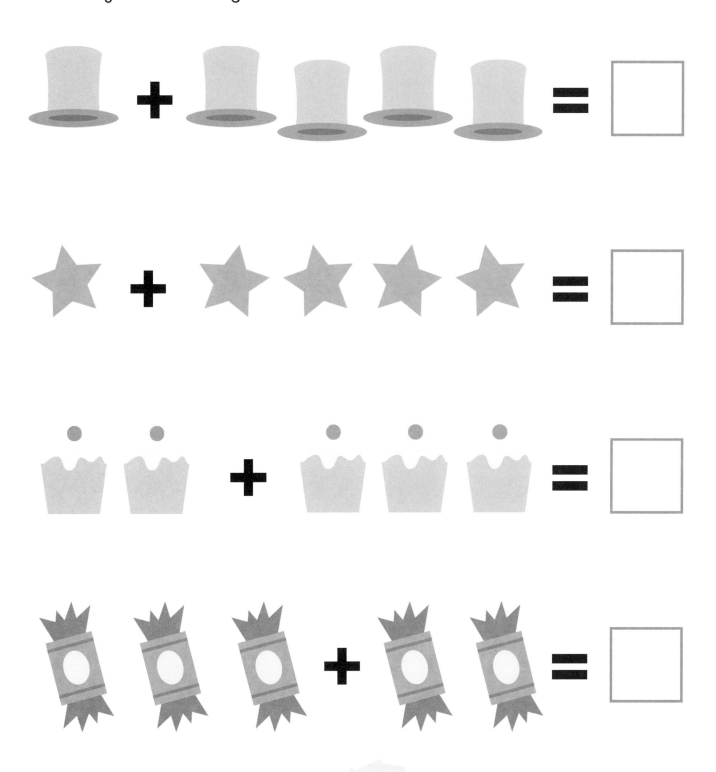

Find a rosette sticker.
The answer to these adding
sums is on the rosette.
Were your sums correct?

Place your
sticker here

Place your
reward sticker
here

Take away 1

Sometimes we want to make numbers less so we take away.

Take away **1** thing from each line by crossing it out.
How many things are left in each line?
Write the number in the box.

Five teds in a bed

Find a teddy sticker.

This is a funny song. Can you learn it?

Place your sticker here

There were **5** in the bed and the little one said,
"Roll over, roll over."
So they all rolled over and one fell out.

There were **4** in the bed and the little one said,
"Roll over, roll over."
So they all rolled over and one fell out.

There were **3** in the bed and the little one said,
"Roll over, roll over."
So they all rolled over and one fell out.

There were **2** in the bed and the little one said,
"Roll over, roll over."
So they all rolled over and one fell out.

There was **1** in the bed and the little one said,
"Goodnight!"

Place your reward sticker here

Take away 2

Take away **2** things from each line by crossing them out.
How many are left?

When we take away things, the number gets less
and we have less.

Find a sticker of 2 pot plants. Can you do the sum?

Place your sticker here **+** **=** Place your reward sticker here

Take away 3

Here are some more take away sums. Take away **3** from each line.
How many are left? Write the answer in the box.

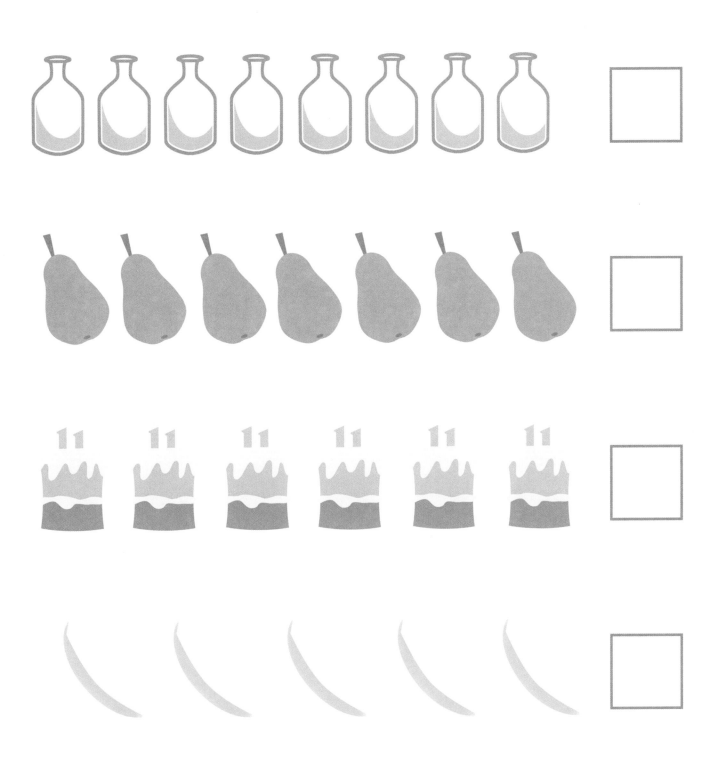

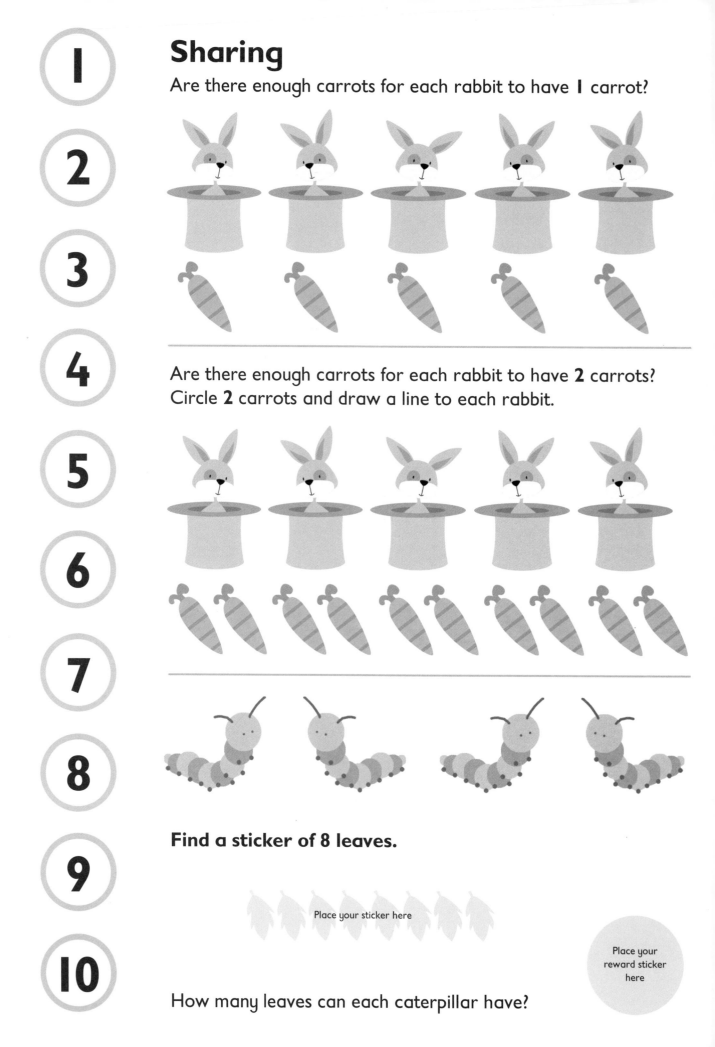

Sharing

Are there enough carrots for each rabbit to have **1** carrot?

Are there enough carrots for each rabbit to have **2** carrots?
Circle **2** carrots and draw a line to each rabbit.

Find a sticker of 8 leaves.

Place your sticker here

Place your reward sticker here

How many leaves can each caterpillar have?

Multiply by 2 and 3

There are **3** children at a picnic. They each have **1** drink, **2** cakes and **3** sausages. Count the things in the picture.

☐ **drinks** ☐ **cakes** ☐ **sausages**

Find a sticker of a sausage.

Place your
sticker here

There were **10** sausages in the pack and the children ate **9**. How many sausages were left?

Place your
reward sticker
here

Can you guess who ate the last sausage?

You are a star!

Find **5** triangles in the star.
Colour these yellow.

Find **1** pentagon in the star.
Colour it red.

Place your
reward sticker
here

Well done! You're a star for finishing this book!